No Vet
Pet

Basic first aid using essential oils

Salina Bhimji

Animal Health Technologist
Bachelor of Science Degree
Animal Aromatherapist
Reiki Master/Teacher
Energy Healing for Animals
Crystal Healing

Creating Health and Wellness within the lives of every pet

Table of Contents

Dedication

I would like to dedicate this book to all those pet owners that desire a holistic way to enhance the health and wellness of their pets.

Disclaimer

The information contained in this book is for educational purposes only. It is not intended as medical treatment, diagnosis, or prescription of any disease. Do not alter any treatment, or the use of any medication without the permission of your medical care provider. Essential oils have been used for centuries with the outcome for helpful benefits, however, individuals should always seek advice from a veterinary health professional. The author of this book takes no responsibility for the misuse of these products. It is the reader's decision to use or not to use any of this information. All recommendations are for Young Living products only.

To Zoe, my cockatiel –
you were and always will
be my world. You will
be greatly missed.

Acknowledgements

I would like to thank my loving husband, Aly Bhimji for believing in me and pushing me to new levels. The amount of love and support you have given me is tremendous.

I would also like to thank my sister, Dr. Alishia Alibhai for always being there every step of the way. You have helped me through all the roadblocks I have encountered throughout my life path.

To my parents - thank you for providing me with the love, support, and encouraging me along any path I chose to take. Thank you all for being there and helping me along with my journey, providing me the strength and courage that I need. I couldn't have done it without your support. You are all truly amazing role models that I admire greatly.

To all my pets – you have all found that special place in my heart. Seeing the benefits of these oils in your lives has given me this strong drive to introduce these oils into every home. Love you all to pieces.

Lastly, I would like to send a special thank you to Dr. Melissa Shelton for her hard work and dedication with helping animals and continuing research on how we can better the health and wellness of our animals with the use of essential oils. I have learned so much from you and admire you greatly.

-Salina Bhimji

Introduction

Ever been to the veterinarian and have had a procedure done on your animal? It can be quite expensive depending on what needs to be done. Some people have found a way to minimize their vet bill and better the health of their pet by using the most natural methods.

Animals are very special beings and tend to find that special place in our hearts. They become a huge part of our family. Animals are very intelligent and know so much more than we know. There is so much to them just by looking into their eyes and they are able to pick up on so many things. Think about when a dog growls at something in the house and you're not sure what it is and then two minutes later someone is at the front door ringing the doorbell. They have such a strong sense, one that has saved the lives of many individuals. We are so lucky to have them in our lives.

Our pets teach us so many things in life. They teach us how to be patient by being patient with us, they teach us how to forgive by forgiving us when we get upset, they teach us loyalty by always being loyal to us and they teach us how to

love by loving us unconditionally. They provide us with so much support with their presence alone and they help us cope and get through those difficult times that can be emotionally, physically, and psychologically draining. This is why animals are brought into long-term care facilities and hospitals. Although animals cannot speak, they definitely have great energy and provide that support that many need and look for.

Many animals that become ill are often taking on illnesses that their owners have. This is often the reason why you see animals resemble their owners.

For example, I have seen numerous animals that have come into the hospital that have heart conditions and later find out that their owners suffer from heart conditions as well. In addition, I have met individuals who have asked me what I would use for their pet who is suffering from cancer. After further conversations with the owner, I realize the owners are battling cancer or other chronic health problems as well. Anxiety is another example. An animal may experience stress and become anxious because they are picking up on the energies of their owners. For example, often times when we are having an 'off' day, our pets sometimes react in odd ways or don't listen or do things they know they are not supposed to. These can all be due to the energies they are picking up on from their owners.

Given how special our pets are to us, we should play our part in making sure that the products we use throughout their lives are of the highest quality, the lowest toxin level, and have the greatest potential for ensuring the health and wellness of our beloved pets. In the pages that follow I will discuss how Young Living Products can be utilized in order to assist our animals in healing and enhancing their life.

The Importance of Young Living Products

Many commercial products on the market these days are being made in mass amounts, thus creating poor quality products. These products contain toxins and cheaper material because it is the cheapest and easiest way to produce these products and allows the distributors to sell them at lower pricing.

When we clean our house and floors with products we buy from the grocery store, use store bought pet shampoos and perfume-filled air fresheners, we are creating a more harmful environment for ourselves and our pets.

Similar to humans, animals take in many substances through the pads of their feet. These are very sensitive areas for animals. We are able to wear shoes to protect any toxins or foreign objects entering through our feet. Animals, on the other hand, are unable to do this thus creating a higher chance of absorbing toxins and unwanted substances into their bodies.

There is great benefit to using Young Living Products (including the oils, the home cleaner, and certain nutritional supplements) on our pets and in our homes. The benefits of these products include: the avoidance of hazardous toxins, the option of internally ingesting the products safely, eliminating airborne bacteria and viruses, and creating a wonderful smelling environment.

Gary Young, the Founder of Young Living Essential Oils, takes great pride in all of Young Living's products. The hard work and dedication that Gary and his team put forth ensure the high quality of the products.

What are Young Living Essential Oils?

Young Living essential oils are the life force energy of plants. They are part of the one percent category in the essential oil market that are 100% natural authentic grade. This is because Young Living is a 'Seed to Seal' company and is responsible for every step of the process: picking the seed, planting, harvesting, distilling and packaging the oil. There is no part of the process that is outsourced; Young Living controls everything that goes into these oils, thus ensuring the high level of purity. If these oils do not meet certain

standards, they are discarded. Young Living's essential oils are either steam distilled or cold pressed and only the initial run off is used thus making it 100% authentic grade.

Young Living's Essential Oils are indeed safe to use on our pets however any other oils that are not Young Living's and are not part of the one percent category of authentic grade oils are not recommended for use on our pets. These essential oils that are not recommended can actually cause more harmful effects on our pets. There are many oils on the market that claim they are 100% pure therapeutic grade however third parties have discovered through testing that not all oils are created equally and that the components may be synthetic, full of fillers and other harmful materials.

Often times individuals experience adverse effects when poor quality oils are made and used so it is very important to ensure the quality of the oils that we use. The recommendations in this book are solely meant for Young Living Essential Oils - using products from other essential oil companies may cause serious harm to pets and their owners and are not recommended.

There is research that has been done and is continuing to be carried out by veterinarians around the world that demonstrate Young Living's essential oils are indeed safe to use on animals. We encourage more of this research and look forward to new and improved findings.

The amount of hard work and labor that goes into making these oils is immense and thus solidifies its great quality. From my experience of helping plant Balsam Fir and Blue Spruce trees at the Highland Flats farm in Naples, Idaho, I was in awe of the amount of work and time that goes into the planting of trees - just one step in the process of producing these oils.

Essential Oil Basics for Pets

To most pet owners, our pets are our children. If your pet has never been introduced to essential oils before, I encourage you to introduce them very slowly. Animals are a lot more sensitive than humans. Because the oils are so potent, the smell and the impact can be quite overpowering for our pets. Consider how police and detectives use search dogs to find the tiniest amount of drugs in large warehouses

or how search and rescue dogs are able to find people that have been buried in two feet of snow in an avalanche. These are great examples of how sensitive our pet's sense of smell is.

Aversions occur when there is a sudden dislike to something or adverse reaction. An aversion to essential oils might occur when an animal is being introduced to an oil too quickly. Once the animal has an aversion, it is very difficult to overcome it therefore the slower you introduce the oils the better. For example, there was a time when my sister was young and she drank a glass of chocolate milk. She wasn't feeling well that day and directly after drinking the chocolate milk, she vomited. After that day she did not drink chocolate milk for a few years for fear of vomiting from it. This is considered an aversion.

In order to avoid aversions, we want to always start with very small amounts of oil until we learn your animal's behavior. Because of the high potency of Young Living's Essential Oils, one drop is plenty to start with, until you are able to read the signs and behavior of whether or not your animal is comfortable with the oils or not.

If you would not use an oil on yourself, then do not begin by using it on your pet first. Always try the oil on yourself before you use it on your pet. With oils that are considered 'hotter oils' such as clove, cinnamon bark or thieves, it may be best to dilute the oil first with a carrier oil and see how your pet does with this before you use it neat or lessen the dilution.

Oils are species specific. This means that some methods that may work best for us may not be the most effective method for a different species. For example, we can drink an oil for the best results, however, that same oil may be used topically for best results on a specific animal.

How to Use Essential Oils on Pets

There are many ways to use essential oils on our pets. Use your own discretion and use methods that work best with your animal. The following are different methods that can be used.

1. Diffusing

Diffusing is a great and gentle way of introducing the oils to our pets. Young Living has great diffusers that can be used for these oils. Ensure that your animal is able to move away from the diffuser if they do not like it or find it too strong.

2. Petting method

Take one drop of oil, rub it on your hands until there is little to no residue left on your palm. Then pet your animal. Avoid petting them in sensitive areas such as on the face, nose, or the bottom of the feet. The petting method is a less irritating method and is in general more tolerated by the animal. It is also an effective method that is a very gentle way to start with if your animal has never been introduced to these oils before.

3. Internally

Dripping one drop of essential oil into your pets food or water. Some animals such as cats may be a bit more finicky when it comes to ingesting oils whereas birds and dogs generally don't seem to mind. Oils are more likely to be ingested if it is mixed with a carrier such as NingXia Red, coconut oil, honey, or red agave. It is best to begin with one drop and see how your animal reacts. You can always add more if they like it.

4. Indirect

Put a drop of oil in your palm and rub it into your hands and then rub your hands on something your pet can approach (such as a piece of furniture or a bed). For example, rub an oil on a perch of a bird cage thus allowing the bird to come to it or rub it on a dog or cat bed. One drop of purification or a purification mist is great in the kitty litter box to reduce any odors. If you do this, be sure to have an additional litter box available to your cat in case they do not like the smell.

5. Water misting

Add water and an oil into a spray bottle. Start with one drop of oil to every four ounces and then you can always increase the amount of oil from there. Oil and water do not mix, however, this method allows it to disperse. Glass bottles are recommended because some Young Living essential oils may degrade plastics.

6. Oil Misting

Mix an oil with a carrier oil in a spray bottle and spray your pet. One drop to every four ounces is a great ratio to start with. If your pet enjoys this, you can increase the amount of oil you add. Avoid any sensitive areas such as scabs or hotspots. We want these areas to dry out and they will not be able to if they remain oily thus continuing to be irritating for the animal.

7. Topically

Allowing one drop of oil to drip right onto the animal. There is no need to part the hair because animals absorb oils through their hair follicles and thus directly into their skin. The oils can either be diluted with a carrier oil (V6 complex or a vegetable oil) or they can be applied neat. Diluting oils that are used on smaller animals such as rodents and birds has been seen in some cases to be more tolerated. This method is not recommended as a first choice for animals that have never been introduced to these oils before.

8. Raindrop

This is a method that involves Tibetan and Lakota healing methods. The oils that are included in this technique are oregano, thyme, basil, peppermint, marjoram, cypress, and wintergreen. Valor can be used at the very start as a primer and balancing oil. Drip the oil onto the fur approximately six inches above the fur. This is to be done from tail to head. Various feathering techniques are then used to drive the oils deeper into the skin. For animals that are more fidgety, the petting method can be used with these raindrop oils.

Signs of Discomfort

Animals speak to us through the use of body language. They always have so much to say. It is a matter of us learning and understanding what they are trying to tell us. By watching them closely and seeing them grow is a great way to learn our pets' behavior. This will eventually allow you to pick up on the slightest behaviors that will indicate to you what they like and dislike.

Often times animals will show signs that clearly indicate they do not like the oils or they are too strong for them. In other instances, these signs may not be quite as obvious. For example, even a slight ear flick back when your pet sees the oil bottle can be a sign of uncertainty. Even the most discrete signs are important to watch for. Some of these signs that we should look for when we are introducing these oils are listed below.

- Sneezing
- Coughing
- Diarrhea
- Itching
- Squinty eyes
- Increase respiratory rate
- Redness around the eyes
- Hiding

- Whale eyes
- Depressed
- Cowering
- Refusing to eat
- Panting
- Running Around
- Ears pinned back
- Tearing

If any of these signs occur, it's recommended that the amount of oil is lessoned and/or the essential oil is diluted.

What To Do and What Not To Do

Do's

Always have a carrier oil present when using essential oils on your pet.
   -V-6 complex
   -Vegetable oil

If your pet has never been introduced to these oils, dilute the oils or begin with very small amounts.

Do not's

Do not apply oils directly to the face, feet, or nose.

Do not use another essential oil to mask the affect of an oil.

If you would not use an oil on yourself, don't use it on your pet.

Do not use water to dilute the oils if the oil irritates the animal. This only drives the oil deeper into the skin.

Dilute hot or irritating oils on your pets (Clove, Thieves, Cinnamon).

Never put an oil directly down the ear canal of an animal. The high potency of these oils can rupture the eardrum and cause a lot of pain and discomfort for your pet.

Important Essential Oil Symptom Guide

Lemon
-Antioxidant
-Anxiety
-Urinary tract infections
-Obesity
-Lipomas
-Digestive complications
-Hypertension
-Cleanse air

Peace and calming
-Anxiety
-Calming
-Hospitalization
-Car rides
-Colic in horses
-Birthing situations
-Obedience training
-Boarding and kenneling
-Depression
-Stress
-Airplane travels

Lavender
-Calming
-Healing
-Burns

-Frostbite
-Parasite repellant
-Skin conditions

Valor
-Courage
-Confidence
-Bravery
-Anxiety
-Stress
-Self-esteem
-Showing
-Competition
-Broken bones
-Joint health

PanAway
-Pain management
-Cruciate injuries
-Arthritis
-Sprains
-Bruising
-Sore muscles
-Joint discomfort
-Increase circulation

Peppermint
-Vomiting
-Arthritis
-Nausea
-Diarrhea
-Anti-parasitic
-Pain relief
-Anti-fungal
-Anti-tumoral
-Anti-inflammatory
-Travel nausea
-Ear mites/Ear
  infections

Thieves
-Immune boosting
-Anti-viral
-Strangles
-Ringworm
-Anti-fungal
-Anti-septic
-Anti-bacterial
-Reducing allergy
  symptoms
-Equine herpes virus
-Reduces allergy
  symptoms
-Anti-inflammatory
-Travel nausea

Purification
-Odors (skunk odors)
-External parasites
-Lacerations
-Upper respiratory
  infections
-Reduce transmission of
  diseases
-Kennel cough
-Insect repellant/bites
-Abscesses

Frankincense
-Lumps
-Tumors
-Cancer
-Cysts
-Seizures
-Depression
-Auto-immune disorders
-Behavioral conditions
-Newborn babies
-Regulation of immune
  system
-Brain disorders

Di-Gize
-Diarrhea
-Vomiting
-Internal parasites
-Colic in horses
-Hairballs
-Deworming

Raven
-Upper respiratory
-Strangles
-Equine herpes
-Anti-viral
-Anti-septic

Aroma Life
-Heart conditions
-Balancing blood
  pressure

Emotional Blends

The following oils can be used for emotional issues; please note that more than one oil can be used for a particular ailment. For example, both Trauma life and Sara can be used for abused animals. Use your intuition - what oil feels right for you, perhaps is the oil that resonates with you or comes into your mind first. Also remember that when I suggest using the essential oil that most resonates with you, it is usually because it is meant to heal both you and your pet as your pet is simply a mirror image of you.

Trauma life
-Animals having surgery
-Abused
-Falling off the bed
-Losing a
  companion/owner
-Entering a
  new home
-Birthing
-Spay/neutering
-Hit by car
-Dog fight
-Branding

Acceptance
-Accepting the present
-Accepting being
  Spayed/Neutered
-Behavioral problems
-New home/Life
-New housemate

Forgiveness
-Past memories
-Rehoming
-Negative events
-Hurt feelings
-Hospitalized
-Boarding
-Neglect and Abuse
-Hit by Car
-Neutering

Sara
-Past abuse
-Puppy Mills
-Breeding
-Repeated surgical
 procedures
-Show animals
-Repeated vet visits
-Competition animals
-Hunting dogs

Release
-Emotional or physical
 release
-Bladder stones
-Cancerous tumors
-Chronic disease
-Constipation

-Difficult labor and
 delivery
-Losing a
 companion/owner

White Angelica
-Protects against
 negative energies and
 thoughts
-Promotes feelings of
 security

Believe
-Shyness
-Separation anxiety
-Thunderstorm activity
-Bone health
-Inflammation
-Cancer
-Showing

Other Important Young Living Products

Animal Scents Shampoo
-Arthritis
-Anti-inflammatory
-Ear or wound flush

Animal Scents Ointment
-Wounds
-Eye conditions
-Insect repellent
-Around incision sites
-Bruising
-Mange

Ortho Ease & Ortho Sport
-Arthritis
-Pain
-Joint pain

-Inflammation
-Sore muscles

Ningxia Red
-Energy
-Bone conditions
-Supports liver function
-Hypoglycemia
-Laminitis
-Diabetes
-Lameness in horses
-Antioxidant
-Boosts immune system
-Detoxifies
-Allergies
-Controls blood sugar
 levels

First Aid for Pets

Animals often get themselves into mischief. Sometimes their curiosity gets the best of them. A great thing to keep on hand when you are traveling with your pet, taking them out to the dog park, or other outdoor excursion is a first aid kit for pets.

The first aid kit should contain the following:

-Animal Sense Ointment
-Peace & Calming essential oil
-PanAway essential oil
-Thieves essential oil
-Purification essential oil
-Peppermint essential oil
-Lavender essential oil
-Raven essential oil
-Di-gize essential oil
-2 Ningxia red packs

-V6 Oil (Carrier Oil)
-Glass spray Bottle
-Square 3 x 3 Gauze
-Gloves
-Gauze bandage
-Bandage scissors
-Bandage tape
-25cc (mL) syringe
-Thieves spray
-Ortho Ease essential oil

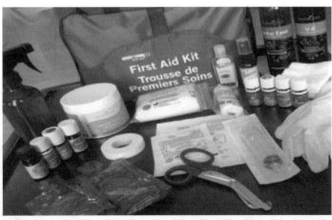

Recipes Using Essential Oils

TREATS

Ningxia Ice Cubes
-In a glass mix 2 tablespoons of Ningxia Red and 4
 ounces of water
-Fill ice tray
-Freeze
-Once frozen serve as a treat

Cinnamon Biscuits
1. Into a bowl add 2 cups whole-wheat flour
2. Add 1 tsp baking powder and mix
3. Add ½ cup water
4. Add 1/8 tsp salt
5. Add 1 large egg and mix
6. Add ¼ cup olive oil
7. Add 1 tsp stevia
8. Add 2 drops of cinnamon essential oil
9. Mix until chunks are gone
10. Preheat oven at 350 degrees
11. Bake at 350 for 15 minutes
12. Let cool before serving

Lemon chicken rice
1. Boil a piece of chicken
2. Make $\frac{1}{4}$ cup of rice (white or brown)
3. Mix 1 piece of chicken with 1 spoon of rice
4. Add $\frac{1}{2}$-1 drop of lemon essential oil
5. Mix and serve

Cinnamon Peanut Butter biscuits
1. Mix 2 cups of whole-wheat flour to $\frac{1}{2}$ cup oatmeal
2. Add 1 drop Cinnamon essential oil
3. Mix $\frac{1}{2}$ cup creamy peanut butter and $\frac{1}{2}$ cup water until it becomes a smooth liquid
4. Combine it with the dry mixture until it becomes dough
5. Evenly space on a cookie sheet
6. Bake at 325 degrees for 15 minutes
7. Let cool before serving

Disinfecting Food Dishes and Toys

Often times we rinse our pet bowls in the sink or throw them into the dishwasher. The mouths of pets can harbor a lot of bacteria. To keep our families and pets from continuously passing germs and bacteria from one another, we want to ensure that we disinfect our pets food bowls, toys and bedding on a regular basis.

Disinfecting beds, cat trees, kennels, carriers, food dishes

1. Use a 27 oz spray bottle
2. Add 2 oz of the thieves household cleaner
3. Fill the rest with water
4. Mix well

Eliminating odors from pet beds, mats, kennels

1. Use a glass spray bottle
2. Add 1 oz baking soda
3. Add 6 drops of purification essential oil
4. Fill the rest with water
5. Shake well

Natural Air Freshener

1. Use a glass spray bottle
2. Add 5 drops of Purification Essential Oil
3. Add 5 drops of Citrus Fresh Essential Oil
4. Fill the rest with water
5. Shake Well

Kitty Litter Box Spray

1. Use a glass spray bottle
2. Add 8 drops of purification
3. Fill the rest with water
4. Mix well
5. Spray in litter box

*Be sure to always have an extra litter box that has not been sprayed just in case your cat does not use the purification smelling litter box.

Eliminating Skunk Smells
1. Use a glass spray bottle
2. Add 1 oz baking soda
3. 10 drops purification
4. 5 drops of Thieves
5. Fill the rest with water
6. Shake well and spray
7. Shampoo with Animal Scents shampoo

Flea/Tick Control
1. Use a 4 oz glass bottle
2. Add 4 drops of Purification
3. Add 4 drops of Citronella
4. Add 1 drop of Cedarwood
5. Add 2 drops of Palo Santo
6. Add 1 drop Thyme
7. Fill the rest with water
8. Shake well

Training

For many individuals, training a puppy or an older dog can be a daunting task. Similarly, trying to eliminate behavioral issues can also be quite frustrating. There are certain essential oils that can be used to help assist in the training process.

One of the main things to remember when training an animal is that consistency is of utmost importance. Animals like consistency and they have more respect for their owners who provide consistency, discipline and re-correction. However, even though consistency, discipline, and re-correction are key, timing is very important. There is no point in disciplining an animal 20 minutes after they have done something wrong because they do not know what they have done wrong at that point.

At the time an animal does something that is not in anyone's best benefit, use the same word and body language that you would for any other poor behavior.

This could be a simple pointer finger shake and a firm 'NO'. Keep this consistent so your pet knows that they have done something wrong at that time.

In addition, one of the main ways to help train your pet is to ensure that your pet follows through with any command you give. Perhaps using an essential oil may help your pet focus on these specific commands (examples are given in the pages that follow). If we tell our dog to sit and walk away before he/she does so, we are teaching our dog that we can say something but he/she does not have to listen. Ensure that the dog is sitting before you walk away. Re-correct if the dog does something different, for example he/she lies down when you said to sit. As soon as he/she displays the appropriate behavior, reward your pet. REWARDING is a very important part of training. It boosts the self-esteem of your pet. Valor is a great oil to help assist in boosting self-esteem and providing courage to overcome any hurdles your pet may encounter.

Often times individuals deal with more difficult issues with their pets. For example, aggression and incontinence, however there are Essential Oils that can help with these problems.

Focus and hyperactivity in our pets is sometimes a very hard thing to ask for in our pets as they want to be involved in everything.

Focusing
-Brainpower
-Peppermint
-Peace & Calming
-Lavender

Hyperactive dogs
-Peace & Calming
-Lavender
-Tranquil

Aggression towards other dogs/animals
-Peace & Calming
-Joy

-Valor
-Surrender

Aggression towards humans
-Trauma life
-Release
-Surrender
-Joy

Fearful
-Valor
-Trauma life
-Release

Energy Healing

Animals respond greatly to various different energies. Often times they are picking up on energies that their owners are giving off. Ever wonder why your pet acts up the most on the days when you are not feeling your best? They are simply reflecting the energies that you are putting out there. I have seen this many times in clinic. A very anxious animal will come into the clinic with their very anxious owners. When I mention to their owner that I will take their pet into the back to perform whatever procedure needs to be done, some owners are quite persistent on accompanying me into the back. The minute I separate the anxious owner from their pet, the animal calms right down.

Often times when we get hurt, we automatically put our hands on that body part that hurts. By doing this we are unintentionally sending energy vibrations from our hands into our body to get the energy flowing. This in turn helps us heal and takes the pain away. This method of healing can be used on our furry babies to help get the energy flowing through their bodies as well. Our touch and our intent can heal many things. Combining this method with essential oils may enhance the healing.

Energy healing is a very powerful non-invasive technique that every individual may perform. There is no right or wrong way of doing this so please be gentle on yourself.

There are many forms of energy healing two of which are my personal favorites are Reiki and Crystal healing.

For those individuals who are interested in these methods, they are great ways to assist in additional healing for your pet.

Testimonials

I noticed my dog, Spirit, limping so I took a look at the pad of her foot. She had a cyst-like lump, which was causing her a lot of pain when I squeezed it. I took her to the vet to see if perhaps she had stepped on a piece of glass. The vet said it was a cyst. At this point she was non-weight bearing. The vet and I did a quick local block and made a very slight poke to ensure that there was no foreign material in her foot. The only material that came out was a pussy, cyst-like substance. The vet mentioned that I could leave it for the time being and if it does not get better then I would have to bring her in for an exploratory surgery. I did not want this because the area where this cyst was located would have been a very difficult place to heal. I told the vet I would do conservative care for a week and see how it goes. He gave me a feeding syringe and some hibitane soap to clean it out a couple times a day.

When I got home I took the syringe and sucked up some thieves. I cleaned her paw with the hibitane soap and then lathered the cyst (inside the tiny hole and around) with thieves. I did this twice a day. After one week the cyst was completely gone.
      -Salina Bhimji

Harlee is a miniature pincher. She developed what I thought was a cyst on the side of her body. I noticed that it was getting larger, so I took her to the vet, and they didn't think it was anything serious however they did say if it got any larger they could cut it off. When I got home I decided I was going to try applying Young Living Frankincense essential oil to it. I put 1 drop in the palm of my non-dominant hand, and activated the frequency by using two fingers clockwise. Then I used the 2 fingers to apply the oil to the cyst. I noticed after the 2nd application that the cyst was shrinking, and within a week it was gone, and it has not returned.

-Nancy McMahon

My mom's dog Mya had an infection around her eyes from an unknown cause. Doctors could not figure out what the cause was. She was constantly pawing at her eyes thus making her eyes more and more infected. She began using the Animal Scents Ointment around her eyes. Mya would calm right down and just sit there because it was a nice release for her eyes. Her scratching decreased within four days.

    - Bailee Comstock-Collinson

 My youngest cockatiel, Charlee, is obsessed with paper bags, business cards, envelopes, and anything made of paper or cardboard! He loves to be out of his cage so that he can explore all the interesting paper and cardboard around the house. Charlee is definitely an "I don't like being in my cage" kind of bird. It's adorable except for when he is locked in his cage; he gets very anxious and upset and continuously screeches as loud as he can to be let out of his cage (even the neighbors have admitted they can hear him!). One time I decided to try peace and calming and lavender essential oils with him. I put one drop of each oil and rubbed it in my palms. I took him out onto my finger for a few minutes so he could soak up the residue from my finger and then I put him back in the cage. He was still a bit anxious at first but after about 5 minutes he had completely calmed down and was

falling asleep in his cage. I now regularly use these two oils with Charlee and he seems to really enjoy them.

-Dr. Alishia Alibhai

I bought a horse in 2008, and found out that when the Ferrier would come to trim her hooves, she would freak out. She would rear up, and flip herself over backwards. We ended up having to lay her down and tie her hooves so she would not hurt herself or anybody working with her. We did this for about 2 years, and then I decided to try applying peace and calming essential oil, and she settled right down. We can now have her hooves trimmed without even tying her up. We are able to just hold her with a lead rope and pet her and talk to her. She is now one of the better horses to trim on our farm.

-Ilieen Fox

One evening, I was trying to cram for a midterm that was the next day. I was trying to focus however I had one cat, "Tat"

chasing my other cat "Molly" and then the dog was chasing Molly and Molly was then hissing at the dog as they do not get along. I decided to take a few drops of peace and calming in my hand and use the petting method on all three of my animals. Within about 10 minutes the two cats were curled up on the couch soundly sleeping and the dog was on her mat out cold dreaming. I went over to the couch and poked at my cats to find that they were in a deep sleep.

    -Salina Bhimji

My dogs have really bad breath. After listening to Salina Bhimji's pet talk, I learned that I could give my pets Young Living essential oils in their water. I put one drop of peppermint and one drop of Thieves oil in their water. At first my dogs did not like it but they got used to it very quickly and their breath is so much better.

    -Anonymous

Our dog Joe (Cool) has had chronic ear infections over the years. Just this week I tried organic coconut oil and Young Living's lavender. I mixed about 3 tsp of the coconut oil and 5-6 drops of lavender. I have given him 2 treatments per day for 2 days and rubbed it around the inside of his ear (the outer part, not right into the ear canal). Then, I gently massaged his ear. The redness has almost gone.

-Lesley Balfour

Some dogs have a body odor that they give off. My dog "Spirit" is a black Labrador and generally has that specific lab smell to her. This is a smell that I am not particularly a fan of. I mist purification, baking soda, and water on her as well as I diffuse purification near her kennel. This takes the smell right out.   -Salina Bhimji

My dog is a 7-month-old Labrador retriever that used to have outbursts of random vomiting. Perhaps he ate something outside, however, I watched him closely when he would go outside. I took one drop of peppermint in my hand and used the petting method, rubbing it all over his stomach. I repeated this three times and have never had this issue with him vomiting again.

-Anonymous

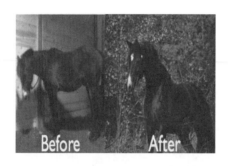

Before   After

R D Kawliga's came to us from an unwanted. He was underweight, full of worms and had a low self-esteem. As we began to work with him, we noticed that he was very quiet, gentle, and accepting of anything we did to him. He would walk around avoiding eye contact, which demonstrated how an abused child would act.

On May 28, 2011, he was bumped by another horse and went through a tensile wire fence ripping both extensor tendons

from the front of his leg. The flexor tendons on the back of his leg were sliced in three different places. He was not weight bearing on his hind leg. The vet said that he would give Liga 2 days and if there was no significant improvement, then he would have to be put down. Illieen fox and myself decided to do a raindrop on Liga using 12 oils instead of 9. We used Peace & Calming, Valor, Oregano, Thyme, Lavender, Lemongrass, Wintergreen, Helichrysum, Sandalwood, PanAway, Aroma Seiz, Peppermint and Ortho Ease massage oil. Dr. Mack told us that the oils would go through the blood stream to where it was needed and that we did not have to put it directly on the sight of injury. We used oils that would battle infection, fever, and depression and promote tissue and muscle regeneration, pain management. Liga was in really bad shape. There was little hope and all we could do was pray for a miracle. A couple days later he was walking at a normal speed with a slight limp only. Further raindrops on Liga led to further healing. July 28, 2011 came around and Liga was almost completely healed and was feeling great about himself. He was confident as ever.

-Ivy Bakken

My dog and cat become very nervous in the car. My dog will sit and whine, howl, and tremble and my cat will meow continuously, vomit, and/or have diarrhea. When I diffuse peace and calming in the car or rub Peace & Calming on them before the car ride these symptoms go away. I have also tried putting a drop of Peace & Calming on their collars and it calms them right down and there are no messes after to clean up. The oils are great.

-Anonymous

I was at a friend's house and she has an over-sized Rottweiler. This dog doesn't realize his size and he is always VERY excited to see people. He thinks he is a lapdog. This one particular time he was overly excited and I was getting to the limit of how much of his excitement I could handle. I pulled out some Peace & Calming and put it just above his nose. It was seconds later he calmed down. It was absolutely amazing, he was a completely different dog.

-Sheryl Fox

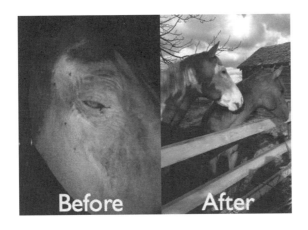

Before / After

Stance is a registered Paint Mare, 13 years old. In early August of 2012 Stance received an eye injury. We called the vet; she came out and treated Stance for a puncture wound in the eye but the wound did not heal. Over the next two days her eye got progressively worse: so much so that we were afraid she would lose the eye. We contacted the vet again and left a message on his cell but he did not return our phone call. We thought it looked a lot like "pinkeye" but had been assured by the vet that horses cannot get "pinkeye." Because the vet's only option was to euthanize, and we were not ready to do this at that time, the vet was not talking to us.

We began Stance on the protocol for pinkeye from the **Essential Oil Desk Reference** compiled by *Life Science Publishing*. The eye started to respond almost immediately. We started Stance on Young Living Essential Oils. We used Eucalyptus Radiata, Lemongrass, Cypress, M-Grain. We used M-Grain for her fever and brain pain on her brain stem and around her ears. The other oils were layered approximately an inch away from the eye. We first applied Eucalyptus Radiata, then cypress and finally lemongrass. The first week we applied it three times per day and the second week two times per day. It was *very important that the oils do not get into the eye.* Stance was barned because the sun bothered her eye. When she went out for walks she wore a UV mask to protect her eye. After two weeks of applying the oils topically we gave her the same 3 oils in her food. She did not have a problem with ingesting the oils. At this time Stance had a scar on her eye but displayed signs of having full vision out of that eye.

     -Brenda Bakken

We have always put oils on our dog Tucker so he is used to smelling them. He is a very hyper dog so he tends to get some scrapes when he goes outdoors and plays in the field. This can happen on a weekly basis. We put lavender oil on his scrapes and they heal up great. Tucker does not mind this at all. Also, recently Tucker had a stomach ache and was eating grass which is a symptom of discomfort, I was worried the strength of the odor of Peppermint would turn him away so I put some on my hands then rubbed it on his tummy and continued to do that a few times that evening. He has been fine ever since.

-Leslee Lundgren

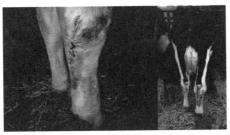 Bonnie Lass is a Purebred Holstein Dairy Cow, Second lactation, 4 years of age. Bonnie developed a bacterial infection in her right hock, which she was being treated with penicillin. The penicillin did not seem to be doing anything for the pain and/or inflammation. Her hock was getting worse. The vet said there was nothing he could do for her so the best option was to "to put her down." After a week I decided to use Ortho Ease massage oil as well as I added anti-inflammatory oils to it. The oils I added were Clove, Thieves, Elemi, Lemongrass, Wintergreen, Thyme, Oregano, and Patchouli. These oils were for pain, fever, and fluid retention. I massaged these oils into her leg and the next day I massaged a mixture of tangerine, cypress, lemongrass, and cellulite massage oil to help reduce the swelling and allow it to drain. After doing a Raindrop treatment on her using Valor, Oregano, Thyme, Marjoram, Cypress, Lavender, Wintergreen,

Lemongrass, Elemi, Thieves, Aroma Seiz, Peppermint and Ortho Ease massage oil, her leg began to drain and continued to drain for a week. Animal Scents Ointment was also used to seal the wound once it broke open. Currently, she is back to normal and eating well.

    -Ivy Bakken

Spotty (white cat - 13 years old) & Puffy (grey cat - 11 years old) Originally my family had 4 cats. After a few years, 1 of my cat's "Tigger" passed away due to an accident. For the last 8 years, Angel, Spotty and Puffy had always had each other. Last March, Angel was diagnosed with diabetes and after a long 9 months we had no choice but to put her down. Since November, Spotty and Puffy have been fighting and attacking each other. Hearing about the Trauma Life Essential Oil, and how it could possibly help animals from Salina Bhimji, we found it beneficial to try and see if this may help our cats after the loss of Angel. A few weeks ago, I began to apply the Trauma Life oil onto the cats. I would put two drops on my hand, rub my hands together, let it air out for about 20 seconds, then ran my hands and fingers through their fur. Almost immediately, Spotty and

Puffy began to acknowledge each other in a more sincere and loving way. Since then, their fighting has almost completely subsided. They are now affectionate and even sleep huddled together.

-April Battenfelder

 Moxy was a Cocker Spaniel, Shih Tzu Poodle cross. Moxy ingested antifreeze and when we took her to the vet her blood was 13. This is extremely low in red blood cells. Normal range for a dog is 37 to 52. The vet recommended to 'put her down' because dogs do not recover from antifreeze poisoning. We decided to put some money into Moxy's recovery. A blood transfusion was done. This brought Moxy's blood up to 24 however her blood cell level continued to decrease for the next 3 days. It went back down to 18. Christmas Eve I was told I could take her home for Christmas for our last goodbyes. When I arrived at home I began using 1 drop of lemon on her paw twice daily to help rebuild red blood cells. On Boxing day, I took her back to the vet for a red blood cell test and it had risen to 24 in 2.5 days. Moxy was granted outpatient status. I kept using lemon and added

grapefruit to our regime of medication in hopes of getting rid of any antifreeze and medications that was left in her. Moxy was still on medication from the vet, which didn't seem to be working without the addition of lemon. We kept Moxy alive for 4 months. Her blood levels were now up to 38. We felt we had overcome the worst and now had to try and get Moxy off the medications the vet had prescribed.
    -Ivy Bakken

I use Valor on my dog who has separation anxiety. I put one drop on her neck fur when I'm leaving and rub it in a little. She still has some anxiety however when I use the oil, there is a huge difference. Her anxiety is so bad she has eaten our blinds, remotes, my shoes, anything plastic left on the counters, and she jumps at the door when we get home. Since using the oils the worse thing we've come home to was an empty pop bottle which had been used as a chew toy. She also sits and waits at the door for us to come in now.
    -Bailee Comstock-Collinson

We are breeders of Registered German Shepherd Pups. We have been breeding since 2004. We generally have large letters of 10 - 12 puppies per litter. On average we have generally lost 1-2 puppies per litter leaving us with 8-10 puppies that grow to be salable puppies at 8 weeks old. In 2009 I decided to start applying frankincense oil to the umbilical cords when they were born, and our survival rate is now 100%.

-Ilieen Fox

About the Author

I discovered Young Living Essential Oils in August 2011 at a wellness festival I attended with my sister. I noticed a big sign that said 'improve your vision', which drew me in. I'm quite skeptical of what I take internally however for some reason I was drawn to this product.

My vision is something that I have struggled with since I was 5 years old. Minus 15 is legally blind – I am minus 10 in one eye and minus 11 in the other. I have had retinal holes with fluid leaking through in both eyes (leading to retinal detachments and blindness if not caught soon enough). I had surgery done on both eyes (laser and creo) to seal the holes. I was also diagnosed with severe corneal stress that was so bad it was affecting my vision. I was using eye drops for my dry eyes over 17 times an hour, a gel 4 times a day, hot compresses at night and a humidifier and still my eyes were chronically blood shot. My face and eyes would hurt because my eyes were so dry. To top things off, now my doctor says I may be approaching borderline glaucoma.

Doctors told me that I would never get any of my vision back and that the only cure for my dry eyes was to move somewhere humid or use a steroidal eye drop.

I began taking Young Living Ningxia red along with the oils and after three weeks my husband began to notice slight differences. My vision was becoming a bit more crisp. I began to notice that I wasn't having such a hard time driving at night and I was not wearing my glasses at night to go to the bathroom.

I went to the eye doctor in January 2012 and he told me that my vision had improved by 0.25. Now in 2014, I'm so grateful to say that my corneal stress has stabilized and I am only using the eye drops once a day, the gel once a day and nothing else.

As an Animal Health Technologist, I have worked in emergency veterinary clinics for many years. I have administered many medications to animals and seen the effects it has had on them. I felt horrible having to give these drugs to these animals and decided that there were other ways to go about helping animals.

I began trying different things on my own animals as well as on my friends animals, with permission of course. I noticed many improvements in short periods of time and it felt so much more fulfilling then drugging them in clinic. I noticed some animals that were suffering would calm right down in my arms.

My passion has always been and will always be for animals and I have realized that my path is now taking me on the more holistic side of helping animals.

My goal is to help introduce these oils into every home in order to enhance the health and wellness of our pets and ourselves.

Visit:
www.novetformypet.com
www.salinabhimji.com

How to order Young Living Products

1. On the internet go to www.youngliving.com or call 1-800-371-2928
2. For online users, choose the Country that you live in
3. At the top right hand corner of the screen, click on member sign-up
4. Scroll down to the bottom of the screen and click on the become a member button
5. Fill out your information
6. Under Enroller and Sponsor ID, you will put the ID number of the person who introduced you to this book with you (simply ask them what their enroller and sponsor number is)

7. You may click on Independent distributor or customer.

      -Independent distributor allows you to buy products at wholesale pricing with no monthly obligation or selling required however if you are interested there is an option to pursue a home-based business. With this you can save anywhere from 24 to 44% off. If you choose to become an independent distributor, choose the kit you wish to purchase (the everyday oil kit contains most of the oils discussed in this book).

      -Becoming a customer allows you to purchase these products at retail pricing. If you choose to become a customer, simply add the items you would like and they will be shipped to you.
8. Click next
9. Continue shopping or complete the ordering process
10. Write down your account number, password and personal identification number. This will help you for future purchases.
11. Your shipment will be sent to your home.

Index

Published and Distrubted by Life Science Publishing
www.lifesciencepublishers.com
1218 South 1850 West, STE A
Orem, Utah 84020

LIFE SCIENCE PUBLISHING™